"I love the name you gave me.
I'd have loved to bring it fame."

(Precious Little One, author unknown)

A special thank you to Whitney for saying "What about a book?" A thank you to Amanda Culley for helping me create the Stinson character that represents our son; Blueberry Illustrations for bringing the images in my head to paper. The biggest THANK YOU to my husband who is on this crazy journey with me, and for supporting me so I could make my dream come true. My kids, all 5 of them, for just being awesome.

Contact Brandi Foster, brandifoster.author@outlook.com

ISBN: 979-8-9859592-0-8
Imprint: Be Kinder Press

Book One in Stinson SAKs collection

Illustrations by Blueberry Illustrations.
Blueberry Illustrations is a world class illustrations and self-publishing company. The illustrators of Blueberry Illustrations are recipients of various awards and nominations. More than 1000 books have been illustrated and published by the company and many more are in the making.
Blueberryillustrations.com

Stinson SAKs

written by

BRANDI FOSTER

Illustrations by

BLUEBERRY ILLUSTRATIONS

Other great ways to use this book:

- Be sure to find Stinson's little butterfly buddy on every page!

- While reading, ask children *"What is the boy doing? How many animals do you see? What sound does that animal make?"*

- Don't feel obligated to write your Simple Acts of Kindness (SAKs) in the back of the book; feel free to discuss with your child instead! My three year old loves talking about kind things he can do for others. He's always so proud when he comes up with a new one!

- Help kids recognize when *others* are performing something kind for them!

Now, SAKs is spelled a little wrong.
"It's spelled all wrong," you say.
"It's supposed to be S-A-C-K-S.
C before the K!"

But these SAKs are different,
and these SAKs are very neat.
They mean you do kind things for others,
using hands and feet.

You do kind things for other people
just because you can.
And Simple Acts of Kindness (SAKs)
will make you a better man!

There was a boy named Stinson.
He was super cute and sweet.
The kind of kid that you'd adore.
To know him was a treat.

Now, Stinson had his daddy's hair
and had his button nose.
He had his mommy's turtle lip
and crooked pinky toes.

Sweet Stinson had a heart of gold
and liked to help others.
He loved his mom and dad so much.
And his sister and brothers.

He walked along and looked for ways
he could make others smile.
He had a gentle presence
and was humble all the while.

He did Simple Acts of Kindness
and always left a note.
"Please pass this kindness on," he said,
that is what he wrote.

Stinson wanted to spread a message
of love and joy around.
He wanted to change the world,
change it by leaps and bounds.

Please Accept this
Simple Act of Kindness!
All I ask is that you
pass it on!

On a warm day in October,
Stinson walked through the zoo.
He thought of Simple Acts of Kindness
There's **SO MANY** he could do!

Stinson heard the loud **BLEATING** first,
and knew it was the goats.

He left some coins for more feed
with one of his little notes.

Stinson saw the giraffes up next.
They knew this boy was neat!

Stinson fed them cantaloupe,
as it was their **FAVORITE** treat!

Stinson found the gray elephants.
To them, he was so nice.

He scratched behind their big ole ears
and each of their trunks twice.

He found the cutest monkeys too
They screeched with great delight
He gave them all a toy to have
and blankies for the night

The monkeys were so fun to play with.
What a **rowdy** bunch!

Stinson's next Simple Act of Kindness
was to buy someone's lunch.

He went to see the lions next
and heard their **boisterous roar!**

He helped to calm them, giving them
BEARS made of velour.

He came upon a few
RED parrots and sang the birds a song.
They became the best of friends; the parrots sang along!

He went to the alligator and saw his

SCARY TEETH!

He found a bench to hide behind,
he couldn't fit underneath!

When he was ready, he came out,
and felt safe going near.
An alligator brushing his teeth?

How Silly!

He's **PROUD!**
He faced his fear!

While Stinson walked around the zoo.
He stopped to take a pause.
Some litter on the ground?

OH MY!!!

Trash was what he saw!

He knelt down and picked up trash
without a hesitation.
Stinson threw it in the garbage,
its proper destination.

Why did Stinson do all these SAKs?
What was such a big deal?

"I want to show EVERYONE
just how LOVE and KINDNESS feel!"

"SAKs are what we are meant to do
to show the world some grace.
Simple Acts of Kindness can make
this world a better place!"

THE END...

or just the beginning?

Do some

Simple Acts of Kindness (SAKs).

There's so many you can do!!!

I can think of

AT LEAST a million.

How many can you?

Write down a few Simple Acts of Kindness (SAKs)
that you can do. I'll get you started!

Hold the door for someone!
____

____

____

____

____

SAKS PERFORMED BY KIDS JUST LIKE YOU!

Help my mom fold laundry. ~Mitchell, 6

Share toys with my sister. ~Leo, 3

Help my mom and dad around the house. ~Max, 9

Put my toys away. ~Hailey, 3

Give someone a high five when they are sad. ~Jocelyn, 9

Give someone a compliment, like telling them they have cool shoes. ~Brantley, 9

Help someone with their work. ~Sadie, 5

Help my grandma take a walk. ~Addie, 8

Hugs and kisses. ~Aubri, 2

Being respectful. ~Sadie H., 5

Can you match the page with the Simple Act of Kindness that was performed?

PAGE	SIMPLE ACT OF KINDNESS
Goat page	Made a friend
Giraffe page	Gave them toys and blankies
Elephant page	Scratched behind their ears
Monkey page	Faced his own fear
Lunch page	Help clean up the earth
Lion page	Left coins for the next person
Parrot page	Gave them their favorite treat
Alligator page	Helped them calm down
Litter page	Bought someone else lunch

ABOUT THE AUTHOR

Brandi is a married mom of five children. The 2 older boys keep her on her toes with their non-stop energy. Her set of boy/girl twins keep her lurking around corners to see what they've gotten into! And her son Stinson, in heaven, keeps her sane and inspires her to write.

She is an occupational therapist by trade, but decided to take on the CHALLENGE of being a stay at home mom a few years ago.

In her free time-there is no free time (see previous info about having kids)!

WANT FREEBIES?

BrandiFosterAuthor.com

FREE downloadable SAKs "Pass Kindness On" cut-out cards!
FREE downloadable activities!
And More!

Did you like the book? Please leave a review on Amazon!

Made in the USA
Columbia, SC
10 January 2023